Pir Attack

by **Jonny Zucker**

illustrated by
Seb Camagajevac

Titles in the Travellers series

Badger Publishing Limited
Oldmedow Road, Hardwick Industrial Estate, King's Lynn PE30 4JJ

Telephone: 01438 791037
www.badgerlearning.co.uk

2 4 6 8 10 9 7 5 3

Pirate Attack ISBN 978 1 84691 851 3

First edition © 2010
This second edition © 2013

Text © Jonny Zucker 2010
Complete work © Badger Publishing Limited 2010

Publisher: David Jamieson
Editor: Danny Pearson
Design: Fiona Grant
Illustration: Seb Camagajevac

Pirate Attack

Contents

Main characters:

Yasin

Mariam,
his sister

Vocabulary:

clanked

crept

lifted

flares

untied

directions

Chapter 1
Dad's Boat

The sky was blue and clear.

The sea was blue and calm.

Yasin and Mariam were on their dad's
boat.

Their dad was a fisherman.

Today was a good day for fishing.

Today there were lots of fish to catch.

"Hey Mariam!" called Yasin.

"Come and help me with this net!"

Mariam ran over to Yasin.

Together they pulled the net in.

It was hard work, but they did it.

There were lots of fish in the net.

"Well done!" called their dad, "that is good work!"

Yasin and Mariam smiled.

"Hey look!" said Mariam.

Another small fishing boat was coming towards them.

"It must be one of Dad's friends!" said Yasin.

"Let's get something to eat," said Mariam.

Chapter 2
Pirates!

Yasin and Mariam went below deck.

Below deck there was a small cabin.

There was some rice to eat.

They ate the rice.

They drank some water.

"Listen," said Mariam, "that other boat
is here."

They heard the other boat clank against their dad's boat.

They heard some people come on board.

They heard people shouting.

They heard their dad shouting.

It was loud and angry shouting.

"That does not sound like Dad's friends," said Yasin.

Mariam put a finger to her lips.

"Let's see what is going on," she said.

Slowly, they crept out of the cabin.

They crept up the steps.

They lifted their heads a tiny bit.

They were shocked by what they saw.

There were two men on board.

The two men were standing over Dad.

He was tied up with ropes.

The men were shouting at him.

They were saying he had to give them his boat.

They were pirates!

Chapter 3
A Plan

Yasin and Mariam began to back down the steps.

Mariam's foot hit one of the steps.

"What was that?" shouted one of the pirates.

He ran down the steps and looked into the cabin.

There was no one there.

He went back up the steps.

Yasina and Mariam came out.

They had been hiding under the table.

"I have an idea," said Yasin.

He found the flares their dad kept on board.

"We will let these off and trap the pirates," he said.

Mariam nodded. "We must save Dad," she said.

Chapter 4
Good Work

Yasin and Mariam crept back on deck.
The pirates were talking on the other
side of the deck.

Yasin ran over and untied Dad.

He whispered the plan to him.

"That is a good plan," Dad whispered
back.

Yasin nodded at Mariam.

Mariam let off the flares in all directions.

The pirates were shocked. They did not know what was going on.

Dad ran over to them and pushed them over.

They fell onto the deck. Dad tied up the first pirate.

Yasin and Mariam tied up the second pirate.

"Good work!" shouted Dad, as he phoned the coastguard.

Twenty minutes later, four coastguards arrived.

They took the pirates onto their ship.

"You were very brave," one of the coast coastguards said to Dad.

"It wasn't me," said Dad, pointing at Yasin and Mariam.

"It was those two!"

Questions:

Where were Yasin and Mariam?

What did Yasin and Mariam have to eat?

How many pirates were there?

Can you name any famous pirates from other books or films?

Shop Shut

by **Jonny Zucker**
illustrated by **Seb Camagajevac**

Contents

18

Main characters:

Jenni – a teenager
from Poland.

Jenni's Dad – a
shopkeeper who
opens a shop in Britain.

Vocabulary:

Polish

empty

posters

special

customer

bought

Chapter 1
Move to Britain

Jenni and her dad lived in Poland.

Her dad owned a food shop.

Lots of Polish people were going to Britain.

There was more work in Britain.

"The shop is empty now," said her dad.

"We will have to move to Britain."

Jenni and her dad moved to Britain.

They went to live in a small town.

Lots of Polish people lived in the town.

Her dad found an empty shop.

"I will open this shop," he said.

The Polish people in the town were happy about the new shop.

But the British people were not happy.

"We do not want a Polish shop," they said.

"We want a British shop."

They tried to get a British person to run the shop.

But nobody wanted to do it.

"I will run this shop," said Jenni's dad.
He put Polish and British food in the shop.

The town's Polish people came to the shop. They loved the Polish food.

But the British people did not come.

"He will only sell Polish food," they said.

Jenni's dad was sad the British people did not come.

"I don't know what to do," he said to Jenni.

Chapter 2
An Idea

Jenni liked living in Britain.

She made lots of friends at school.

She made Polish friends and British friends.

But her dad was not happy.

"I wish the British people came to my shop," he said.

"Do not worry," said Jenni. "I have an idea."

The next day Jenni ran to school.

She had made some posters.

They were posters about the special offers on British food in her dad's shop.

There were also special offers on sweets. And ice creams. And crisps.

Jenni put the posters up all round school.

That day after school, a British boy
called Tom came to the shop.

"What are you doing?" asked his mum.

"There is a special offer on sweets in
this shop," said Tom.

He went inside to buy some sweets.
Jenni's dad was very pleased to see
Tom.

"You are my first British customer!"
he said.

Tom spent a long time in the shop.

He was talking to Jenni and her dad.

Tom's mum waited for ten minutes.

Then she went in.

"I have just come for my son," she said.

She looked around the shop and was amazed.

There was lots of British food in there.

Chapter 3
Busy Shop

"People told me you only sold Polish food," she said.

"Those people never came into the shop," Jenni's dad replied.

Tom's mum bought some British food.

"I will tell everyone about this shop," she said.

Tom's mum told everyone about the shop.

Soon, lots of British people started coming to the shop.

Jenni's dad was very happy.

Now Polish and British people came to the shop.

But soon there were not so many jobs in Britain.

"There is more work in Poland," the Polish people said.

Chapter 4
Please Stay!

Lots of Polish people moved back to Poland.

"We will have to move back to Poland," said Jenni's dad.

But Jenni liked living in Britain.
She spoke to all of her British friends at school.

They spoke to their parents.

The British people wrote a letter to Jenni's dad.

"Please stay," they said. "We like having a Polish person running this shop!"

Jenni's dad was very happy. "Okay," he laughed. "We will stay!"

Questions

What country are Jenni and her dad from?

Why weren't British people coming into their shop?

What items were on special offer?

What things would you sell if you owned a shop?